The RIDDLE Book

Compiled by OSCAR WEIGLE

Pictures by JOHN HUEHNERGARTH

GROSSET & DUNLAP · Publishers · NEW YORK

Library of Congress Catalog Card Number: 67-23804

Who took the first taxi ride in American history?
George Washington. He took a hack at the cherry tree.

What is a panther?
A man who makes panth.

What must you do if a dog chews a dictionary?
Take the words right out of his mouth.

What do they call a spy in China?
A Peking Tom.

What goes up and down, yet never touches sky or ground?
A pump handle.

What is black on the inside, white on the outside, and hot?
A wolf in sheep's clothing.

Why did the fly fly?
Because the spider spied 'er.

What lives in winter, dies in summer,
 and grows with its roots upward?
An icicle.

Why are some children like flannel?
Because they shrink from washing.

How many monkeys can
  you put into an
  empty barrel?
*One. After that the
  barrel isn't empty.*

Why is winter the best time to buy thermometers?
Because in summer, they are higher.

What did George Washington say to his men before crossing the Delaware?

"Get in."

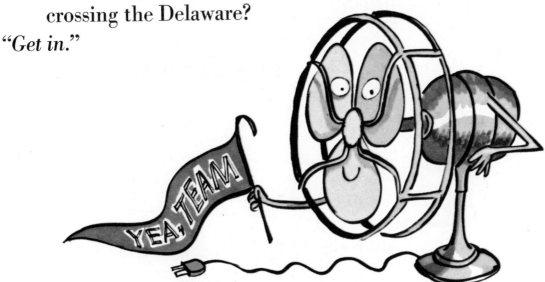

Why is it always cool in sports arenas?
Because there are fans in every seat.

What is the difference between the land and the ocean?
The land is dirty and the ocean is "tidy."

What should you do when you are presented with a
     marble cake?
Take it for granite.

What is raised in Brazil during the rainy season?
Umbrellas.

Why did the cookie cry?
Because its mother had been a wafer so long.

What do animals do when they lose their tails?
They go to a retail store.

Why did the sleepy boy take a hammer to the barn loft?
To hit the hay.

What would happen if you crossed a chicken and a poodle?
The chicken would lay pooched eggs.

If the night has a thousand eyes, what has a thousand ears?
A cornfield.

What is the best thing to take when you're run down?
The license number of the car that hit you.

Who gets paid for never doing a day's work?
A night watchman.

What always works with something in its eye?
A needle.

What happens to ducks when they fly upside-down?
They quack up.

What's the difference between a big hill and a big pill?
One is hard to get up; the other is hard to get down.

What did Paul Revere say after his ride?
"Whoa!"

What makes the Tower of Pisa lean?
It doesn't eat enough.

Why do rabbits have shiny noses?
Because their powder puffs are at the wrong end.

What did the highway say to the road?
"Do you ever get that run-down feeling?"

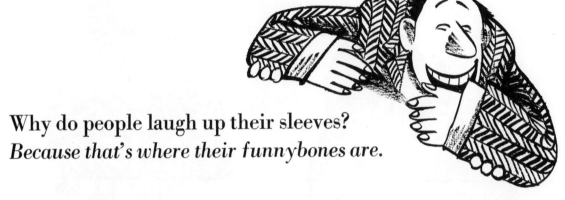

Why do people laugh up their sleeves?
Because that's where their funnybones are.

What ten-letter word starts with gas?
Automobile.

Which is the most difficult train to catch?
They're all about the same if you let them start first.

How can you carry water in a sieve?
Freeze it.

What has a thousand needles but does not sew?
A porcupine.

Why does a carpenter value his hands?
Because they have nails.

What is the best way to keep dogs out of the streets?
Put them in a barking lot.

What happens when you feed lemons to a cat?
You get a sour puss.

Why do some babies' hair turn white while they are
    still infants?
*Because they have nearsighted mothers who keep
    powdering the wrong end.*

When do the leaves begin to turn?
When the teacher announces a test for the next day.

What is the hardest thing in the world to deal with?
An old deck of cards.

Who always whistles while he works?
A traffic policeman.

What happens after a dry spell?
It rains.

How long will an eight-day clock run without winding?
It won't run at all without winding.

What do you have when a bird flies into a lawn mower?
Shredded tweet.

What has a foot on each end and one in the middle?
A yardstick.

What bird is present, but never seen, at every meal?
The swallow.

When are eyes not eyes?
When a sharp wind makes them water.

What must you do before getting off a merry-go-round?
Get on it.

What is green, noisy and
      extremely dangerous?
A stampeding herd of pickles.

How high do people usually stand?
Over two feet.

What did the bald man say when he got a comb for a present?
"Thank you very much. I'll never part with it."

What usually happens when there is a big flood?
A river gets too big for its bridges.

When is a dollar like a shirt?
When it's changed.

What is often plowed, but never planted?
Snow.

Why has Santa Claus taken up gardening?
Because he likes to hoe, hoe, hoe!

What comes after a snowstorm?
Snow shovels.

Why does a baby duck walk softly?
Because it can't walk hardly.

Why do weeping willows weep?
Because they're not pine trees. If they were, they would pine.

What is a coquette?
A small Coca-Cola.

Who sells ice cream in Arizona?
Good Yuma men.

What works when it plays, and plays when it works?
A fountain.

What is always behind time?
The back of a clock.

What does "tempest in a teapot" mean?
It means a storm is brewing.

Why did the elephant swallow a mothball?
To keep moths out of his trunk.

What happens to a man who doesn't know
toothpaste from putty?
All of his windows fall out.

When is an elevator a big disappointment?
When it lets you down.

What happens when the human body is submerged in water?
The telephone rings.

What is the best way to catch a squirrel?
Climb a tree and act like a nut.

Why is tennis a noisy game?
Because each player raises a racket.

What did the airplane pilot say as he flew over the Riviera?
"That's Nice."

What do you make when you put two banana peels together?
A pair of slippers.

Why does a sick person lose his sense of touch?
Because he doesn't feel well.

What did the grape say as the elephant stepped on it?
It didn't say a word. It just let out a little wine.

How can you have a set of teeth inserted free?
Tease a watchdog.

What did the calf say to the silo?
"Is my fodder in there?"

Why is a pig's tail like getting up at four o'clock in
    the morning?
It's twirly.

What makes opening a piano so difficult?
The keys are on the inside.

When is it correct to serve milk in a saucer?
When you're feeding the cat.

How does the wind blow in the spring?
Easter-ly.

If an athlete gets athlete's foot, what does an astronaut get?
Missile toe.

What is black and white and has fuzz inside?
A police car.

Why is it easier to clean a mirror than a window?
A window must be cleaned on both sides.

The cabbage, the garden hose and the tomato decided to have a race. How did it go?

The cabbage was ahead, the hose was running, and the tomato was trying to catsup.

What day of the year is a command to go forward?

March 4th.

Why do pigs eat so much?

Because they want to make hogs of themselves.

What kind of ants are found in a house?
Occup-ants.

When is a boat affectionate?
When it hugs the shore.

Why do dentists tend to get fat?
Practically everything they touch is filling.

If a man were to take a sledge hammer and smash a clock,
would he be accused of killing time?
Not if the clock struck first.

What starts with E and ends with E and has one letter in it?
An envelope.

When Big Chief Shortcake died, what did his widow say?
"Squaw bury Shortcake."

Why should you never try to sweep out a room?
*Because it's too big a job. Just sweep out the dirt and
leave the room there.*

How do you keep a rhinoceros from charging?
Take away his credit card.

What is a rabbit called who has never
been outside the house?
An ingrown hare.

How does a clever Boy Scout start a fire with two sticks?
He makes certain that one of them is a match.

What is the best way to keep water from running into
the house?
Don't pay the water bill.

What does an envelope say when you lick it?
Nothing. It just shuts up.

How can you turn a pumpkin into a squash?
Throw it up in the air. It will come down—SQUASH!

What did one candle say to the other?
"Are you going out tonight?"

When will water stop running downhill?
When it reaches the bottom.

How can you always be two
    jumps ahead of the
    next fellow?
Play checkers with him.

Why does a traffic signal turn red?
You would, too, if you had to change in front of all
those people.

Why would George Washington find it hard to throw a
silver dollar across a river nowadays?
Money doesn't go as far as it used to.

What did one tonsil say to
the other tonsil?
"Better get ready—the doctor is taking us out."

Why did the little boy lock his father in the refrigerator?
Because he wanted cold pop.

Why are playing cards like wolves?
Because they come in a pack.

Why should girls never learn a foreign language?
Because one tongue is enough for any woman.

Why is a warm day bad for an icicle's character?
It turns the icicle into an eavesdropper.

Why is a hive like someone watching?
Because it's a bee-holder (beholder).

February brings snow;
March brings the spring;
April brings showers—
What do May flowers bring?
Pilgrims.

When is silence all wet?
When it reigns.

What is the end of everything?
The letter G.

What candy bar is only for girls?
Hershey. (Her-she)

What's green and walks through walls?
Casper the friendly cucumber.